POEMS FOR
8 YEAR OLDS

Susie Gibbs has worked in the world of children's poetry for ten years. Her eight nephews and nieces were invaluable testing grounds for *Poems for 8 Year Olds*, and she very much hopes that their contemporaries will enjoy this selection. Having recently taken her narrowboat, *Hesperus II*, to Wigan Pier and back, Susie now lives aboard it on the River Thames with no pets but plenty of wildlife.

Anna C. Leplar has illustrated numerous children's books, both in England and in Iceland where she lives with her family.

POEMS FOR 8 YEAR OLDS

CHOSEN BY
Susie Gibbs

ILLUSTRATED BY
Anna C. Leplar

MACMILLAN CHILDREN'S BOOKS

Dedicated with love to all my nephews and nieces:
George Henry Cormick, Nicholas John, Mustafa Noah, Lütfiye,
Patrick Charles, Hatice Sara, Ayse Filiz and
Zenda Amy Lily Sunshine.

First published 1999
by Macmillan Children's Books
a division of Macmillan Publishers Ltd
25 Eccleston Place, London SW1W 9NF
Basingstoke and Oxford
www.macmillan.co.uk

Associated companies throughout the world

ISBN 0 330 37183 5

1 3 5 7 9 8 6 4 2

A CIP catalogue record for this book is available from the British Library.

Printed by Mackays of Chatham plc, Chatham, Kent.

Contents

Secret — *John Agard*   1

A Saying from Zimbabwe — *Anon*   2

The Disco Sheep — *John Coldwell*   3

Tadpoles — *Peter Dixon*   4

The Birthday Cake — *Colin West*   5

'Ware Tomato-Juice — *Anon*   6

Stickleback — *Ted Hughes*   7

Thy Servant a Dog — *Rudyard Kipling*   8

Good Morning This is the
Teacher Forecast — *David Calder*   10

Purple — *Jeff Moss*   11

Lines by a Humanitarian — *Anon*   12

School Dinners — *Anon*   13

Good Morning,
Mr Croco-doco-dile — *Charles Causley*   14

Birthdays — *James Emtage*   16

See You Later, Alligator — *Anon*   17

Glenis — *Allan Ahlberg*   18

Pussycat, Pussycat — *Max Fatchen*   19

New Leaf — *Mick Gowar*   20

The Night of Trafalgar — *Thomas Hardy*   23

The Pantomime — *Guy Boas*   26

Square Meal — *Adrian Henri*   27

Beachcomber — *George Mackay Brown*   28

If You Should Meet a Crocodile – *Anon*   31

Wanted – a Witch's Cat – *Shelagh McGee*   32

The Trick – *John Mole*   34

Den to Let – *Gareth Owen*   36

Is the Moon Tired? – *Christina Rossetti*   40

Sunday in the Yarm Fard – *Trevor Millum*   42

Victoria's Poem – *Fred Sedgwick*   43

I Saw a Jolly Hunter – *Charles Causley*   44

Kisses! – *Ian Souter*   45

Smile – *Matthew Sweeney*   47

Christmas Pudding – *Charles Thomson*   48

Give Yourself a Hug – *Grace Nichols*   52

An Accident – *Wes Magee*   53

A Better Mousetrap – *Anon*   55

I Saw a Ship a-Sailing – *Anon*   56

The Fibber – *Lindsay MacRae*   58

The Lobster Quadrille – *Lewis Carroll*   60

Otter – *Calum Brown*   62

Ode to a Sneeze – *Anon*   63

Pet Shop – *Leonard Clark*   64

Chips – *Stanley Cook*   65

Short Poem – *Steve Turner*   66

Small, Smaller – *Russell Hoban*   67

Electric Full Stops! – *Nisha Doshi*   68

The Woodman's Dog – *William Cowper*   69

Cat! – *Eleanor Farjeon*   70

The Story of Augustus Who Would
  Not Have Any Soup – *Heinrich Hoffmann*   72

My Dad the Headmaster – *Paul Cookson*   74

The Cat's Muse – *Philip Gross*   76

Alone – *David Harmer*   79

I Dream of a Time – *John Foster*   82

Rat it Up – *Adrian Mitchell*   83

Way Down South – *Anon*   87

What Teachers Wear in Bed! – *Brian Moses*   88

There Was An Old Man... – *Edward Lear*   90

The Land of Counterpane – R. L. Stevenson   91

The Pobble Who Has No Toes – *Edward Lear*   92

The Child Who Pretended to
  be a Dragon – *Nick Toczek*   94

Longing – *Anon*   96

Football Through the Ages – *Celia Warren*   97

The Camel – *Ogden Nash*   98

Lines – *Judith Nicholls*   99

I Think I Could Turn and Live
  With Animals – *Walt Whitman*   100

Someone Stole The – *Brian Patten*   101

Daisies and Grasses – *Anon*   102

Amy Elizabeth Ermyntrude
  Annie – *Queenie Scott-Hopper*   103

Down With Flu! – *Matt Simpson*   104

Pool Players – *Kit Wright*   106

Snow – *Edward Thomas*   108

Polly – *Anon*   109

Four Little Tigers – *Frank Jacobs*   110

Thirty Days Hath September – *Anon*   112

The Codfish – *Anon*   113

Say, Did You Say? – *Anon*   114

Secret

Tell me your secret.
I promise not to tell.
I'll guard it safely at the bottom of a well.

Tell me your secret.
Tell me, tell me, please.
I won't breathe a word, not even to the bees.

Tell me your secret.
It will be a pebble in my mouth.
Not even the sea can make me spit it out.

John Agard

A Saying from Zimbabwe

If you can walk
You can dance
If you can talk
You can sing

Anon

The Disco Sheep

The disco sheep danced down the street.
He stomped his hooves to a disco bleat.

'I'm Sam the Ram. So form a queue.
I'll dance with ewe and ewe and ewe.

'I'm the best at The Hip Hop Skip.
Your number one at The Sheep Dip Trip.

'All you sheep wherever you are,
Shout Sam the Ram – Superbaah.'

John Coldwell

Tadpoles

Said the tadpole to the tadpole
as they tadpoled round their jar
I don't want to be a froggy
I don't want to grow that far.
I'm happy as I am now
black blob and little tail,
I don't want to be a froggy
or a toady
or a whale.

I just want to be a taddy
I want to stay the same,
I liked being frogspawn
I didn't want to change . . .
Oh, why've I got to grow up
and be an ugly toad,
creep around in ditches
 — and get squashed in the road.
I'd like to stay a taddy
Stay the same for life.
This jar can be my palace . . .

    and you can be my wife.

Peter Dixon

The Birthday Cake

O why did Mavis have to make
Me such a soppy birthday cake,
With icing pink and ribbon red?
Why couldn't she have made instead
A cake of which I could be proud –
Aren't FA Cup-shaped ones allowed?

Colin West

'Ware Tomato-Juice

An accident happened to my brother Jim
When somebody threw a tomato at him —
Tomatoes are juicy and don't hurt the skin,
But this one was specially packed in a tin.

Anon

Stickleback

The Stickleback's a spiky chap,
  Worse than a bit of briar.
Hungry Pike would sooner swallow
  Embers from a fire.

The Stickleback is fearless in
  The way he loves his wife.
Every minute of the day
  He guards her with his life.

She, like him, is dressed to kill
  In stiff and stecly prickles,
And when they kiss, there bubbles up
  The laughter of the tickles.

Ted Hughes

Thy Servant a Dog

There is walk-in-the-Park-on-lead. There is off-lead-when-we-come-to-the-grass. There is 'nother dog, like me, off-lead. I say: 'Name?' He says: 'Slippers.' He says: 'Name?' I say: 'Boots.' He says: 'I am fine dog. I have Own God called Miss.' I say: 'I am very fine dog. I have Own God called Master.' There is walk-round-on-toes. There is Scrap. There is Proper Whacking. Master says:

'Sorry! Awfully sorry! All my fault.' Slippers's
Miss says: 'Sorry! My fault too.' Master says: 'So
glad it is both our faults. Nice little dog, Slippers.'
Slippers's Miss says: 'Do you really think so?'
Then I make 'Beseech'. Slippers's Miss says:
'Darling little dog, Boots.' There is on-lead again,
and walking with Slippers behind both Own
Gods, long times . . . Slippers is not-half-bad dog.
Very like me. 'Make-fine-pair,' Master says . . .

Rudyard Kipling

Good Morning This is the Teacher Forecast

Mrs Brown
will be gloomy with occasional outbreaks of rage,
storms are expected by mid-afternoon

Miss Green
will be mild, although her smiles
will probably cloud over when she finds
the spider in her chalk box

Mr White
will be rather windy, especially after dinner-time,
with poor visibility when his glasses fog over

Some drizzle is expected around Miss Red,
she has not quite got over her cold,
and Mrs Blue is already gusting down the corridor
and should reach gale force 9 when she hits the
    playground.

For the rest of you, it will be much as usual,
a mixture of sunny moments and sudden heavy
    showers.
Have a good day.

David Calder

10

Purple

If purple was the only colour in the world . . .
You would read about 'Snow Purple and The
   Seven Dwarfs'.
You would sing about
   'The Purple Grass Growing All Around, All
   Around',
And you would drink purple juice for breakfast.
You'd write with chalk on the purpleboard,
And cross the street when the light turned purple,
And visit the President of the United States in the
   Purple House.
You could even write a poem that begins:

Roses are purple, violets are purple . . .

It's a good thing there are other colours.

Jeff Moss

Lines by a Humanitarian

Be lenient to lobsters, and ever kind to crabs,
And be not disrespectful to cuttlefish or dabs;

Chase on the Cochin-China, chaff not the ox obese
And babble not of feather-beds in company with
　　geese.

Be tender with the tadpole, and let the limpet
　　thrive,
Be merciful to mussels, don't skin your eels alive;

When talking to a turtle, don't mention calipee* –
Be always kind to animals wherever you may be.

Anon

* Calipee is turtle soup.

School Dinners

If you stay to school dinners
Better throw them aside;
A lot of kids didn't
A lot of kids died.

The meat is made of iron,
The spuds are made of steel;
And if that don't get you
The afters will!

Anon

Good Morning,
Mr Croco-doco-dile

Good morning, Mr Croco-doco-dile,
And how are you today?
I like to see you croco-smoco-smile
In your croco-woco-way.

From the tip of your beautiful croco-toco-tail
To your croco-hoco-head
You seem to me so croco-stoco-still
As if you're croco-doco-dead.

Perhaps if I touch your croco-cloco-claw
Or your croco-snoco-snout,
Or get up close to your croco-joco-jaw
I shall very soon find out.

But suddenly I croco-soco-see
In your croco-oco-eye
A curious kind of croco-gloco-gleam,
So I just don't think I'll try.

Forgive me, Mr Croco-doco-dile
But it's time I was away.
Let's talk a little croco-woco-while
Another croco-doco-day.

Charles Causley

Birthdays

I'm not going to invite you to my party,
Why not?
Because you did not invite me to yours,
I did not invite you to mine because I don't like you,
Why don't you like me?
Because you never invited me to your party
Okay I will invite you to my party
And I will invite you to my party
Okay when is yours?
Tomorrow, when is yours?
It was yesterday.

James Emtage (8)

See You Later, Alligator

See you later, alligator.
In a while, crocodile.
See you later, hot potato.
If you wish, jelly-fish.
Not too soon, you big baboon.
Toodle-oo, kangaroo.
Bye-bye, butterfly.
See you tomorrow, horror.
In a week, freak.

Anon

Glenis

The teacher says:

Why is it, Glenis,
Please answer me this,
The only time
You ever stop talking in class
Is if I ask you
Where's the Khyber Pass?
Or when was the Battle of Waterloo?
Or what is nine times three?
Or how do you spell
Mississippi?
Why is it, Glenis,
The only time you are silent
Is when I ask you a question?

And Glenis says:

Allan Ahlberg

Pussycat, Pussycat

Pussycat, pussycat, where have you been,
Licking your lips with your whiskers so clean?
Pussycat, pussycat, purring and pudgy,
Pussycat, pussycat. WHERE IS OUR BUDGIE?

Max Fatchen

New Leaf

Today is the first day of my new book.
  I've written the date
    and underlined it
      in red felt-tip
        with a ruler
I'm going to be different
    with this book.

    With this book
  I'm going to be good.
    With this book
I'm always going to do the date like that
      dead neat
    with a ruler
  just like Christine Robinson.

With this book
I'll be as clever as Graham Holden,
  get all my sums right, be as
    neat as Mark Veitch;
I'll keep my pens and pencils
    in a pencil case
and never have to borrow again.

With this book
I'm going to work hard,
not talk, be different —
  with this book,
not yell out, mess about,
  be silly —
    with this book.

With this book
  I'll be grown-up, sensible,
  and everyone will want me;
    I'll be picked out first
    like Ian Cartwright:
no one will ever laugh at me again.
    Everything will be
      different

  with this book . . .

Mick Gowar

The Night of Trafalgar

In the wild October night-time, when the wind
    raved around the land,
And the Back-sea met the Front-sea, and our
    doors were blocked with sand,
And we heard the drub of Dead-man's Bay, where
    bones of thousands are,
We knew not what the day had done for us at
    Trafalgar.
        Had done,
        Had done,
      For us at Trafalgar!

'Pull hard, and make the Nothe, or down we go!'
    one says, says he.
We pulled; and bedtime brought the storm; but
    snug at home slept we.
Yet all the while our gallants after fighting
    through the day,
Were beating up and down the dark, sou'-west of
    Cadiz Bay.
        The dark,
        The dark,
      Sou'-west of Cadiz Bay!

The victors and the vanquished then the storm it
　　tossed and tore,
As hard they strove, those worn-out men, upon
　　that surly shore;
Dead Nelson and his half-dead crew, his foes from
　　near and far,
Were rolled together on the deep that night at
　　Trafalgar!
　　　　The deep
　　　　The deep,
　　　That night at Trafalgar!

Thomas Hardy

The Pantomime

Regularly at Christmas-time
We're taken to the Pantomime;
We think it's childish, but we go
Because Papa enjoys it so.

Guy Boas

Square Meal

He kept a pet hyena
And then he bought a flock
He fed them all on Oxo cubes
And made a laughing stock.

Adrian Henri

Beachcomber

Monday I found a boot —
Rust and salt leather.
I gave it back to the sea, to dance in.

Tuesday a spar of timber worth thirty bob.
Next winter
It will be a chair, a coffin, a bed.

Wednesday a half can of Swedish spirits.
I tilted my head.
The shore was cold with mermaids and angels.

Thursday I got nothing, seaweed,
A whale bone,
Wet feet and a loud cough.

Friday I held a seaman's skull,
Sand spilling from it
The way time is told on kirkyard stones.

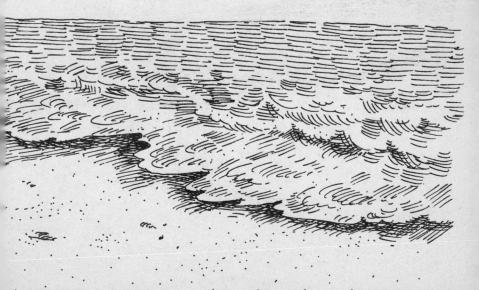

Saturday a barrel of sodden oranges.
A Spanish ship
Was wrecked last month at The Kame.

Sunday, for fear of the elders,
I sit on my bum.
What's heaven? A sea chest with a thousand gold
    coins.

George Mackay Brown

If You Should Meet a Crocodile

If you should meet a crocodile,
    Don't take a stick and poke him;
Ignore the welcome in his smile,
    Be careful not to stroke him.
For he sleeps upon the Nile,
    He thinner gets and thinner;
But whene'er you meet a crocodile
    He's ready for his dinner.

Anon

Wanted - A Witch's Cat

Wanted — a witch's cat.
Must have vigour and spite,
Be expert at hissing,
And good in a fight,
And have balance and poise
On a broomstick at night.

Wanted — a witch's cat.
Must have hypnotic eyes
To tantalize victims
And mesmerize spies,

And be an adept
At scanning the skies.

Wanted — a witch's cat,
With a sly, cunning smile,
A knowledge of spells
And a good deal of guile,
With a fairly hot temper
And plenty of bile.

Wanted — a witch's cat,
Who's not afraid to fly,
For a cat with strong nerves
The salary's high.
Wanted — a witch's cat;
Only the best need apply.

Shelagh McGee

The Trick

One night, when I couldn't sleep,
My Dad said
Think of the tomatoes in the greenhouse

And I did.
It wasn't the same as counting sheep
Or anything like that.

It was just not being in my room forever
On a hot bed
Restless, turning and turning,

But out there, with the patient gaze of moonlight
Blessing each ripe skin
And our old zinc watering-can with its sprinkler,

Shining through a clear glass pane
Which slowly clouded over into
Drowsy, comfortable darkness

Till I woke and came downstairs to breakfast
Saying *Thank you, Dad,*
I thought of them. It did the trick.

John Mole

Den to Let

To let
One self-contained
Detached den.
Accommodation is compact
Measuring one yard square.
Ideal for two eight-year-olds
Plus one small dog
Or two cats
Or six gerbils.
Accommodation consists of:
One living-room
Which doubles as kitchen
Bedroom
Entrance-hall
Dining-room
Dungeon
Space Capsule
Pirate boat
Covered wagon
Racing car
Palace
Aeroplane
Junk-room
And lookout post.

Property is southward facing
And can be found
Within a short walking distance
Of the back door
At bottom of garden.
Easily found in the dark
By following the smell
Of old cabbages and tea-bags.
Convenient escape routes
Past rubbish dump
To Seager's Lane
Through hole in hedge,
Or into next door's garden;
But beware of next door's rhinoceros
Who sometimes thinks he's a poodle.
Construction is of
Sound corrugated iron
And roof doubles as shower
During rainy weather.
Being partially underground,
Den makes
A particularly effective hiding place
When in a state of war
With older sisters
Brothers
Angry neighbours
Or when you simply want to be alone.
Some repair work needed
To north wall

Where Mr Spence's foot came through
When planting turnips last Thursday.
With den go all contents
Including:
One carpet — very smelly
One teapot — cracked
One woolly penguin —
No beak and only one wing
One unopened tin
Of sultana pud
One hundred and three Beanos
Dated 1983–1985
And four Rupert annuals.

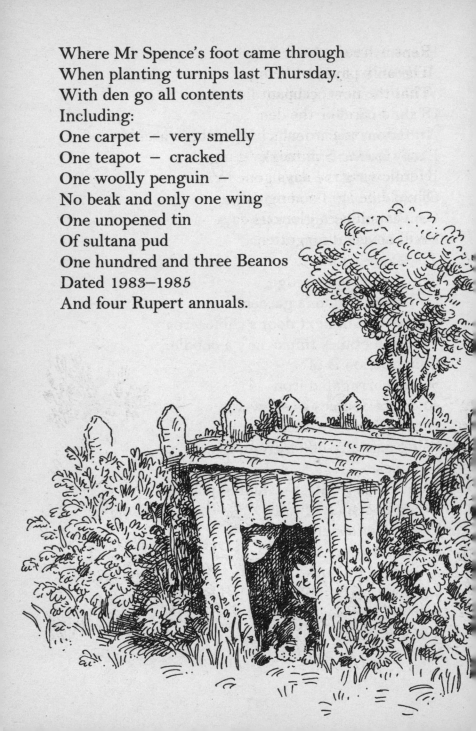

Rent is free
The only payment being
That the new occupant
Should care for the den
In the manner to which it has been accustomed
And on long Summer evenings
Heroic songs of days gone by
Should be loudly sung
So that old and glorious days
Will never be forgotten.

Gareth Owen

Is the Moon Tired?

Is the moon tired? She looks so pale
Within her misty veil;
She scales the sky from east to west,
And takes no rest.

Before the coming of the night
The moon shows papery white;
Before the dawning of the day,
She fades away.

Christina Rossetti

Sunday in the Yarm Fard

The mat keowed
The mow cooed
The bog darked
The kigeon pooed

The squicken chalked
The surds bang
The kwuk dacked
The burch rells chang

And then, after all the dacking and the changing
The chalking and the banging
The darking and the pooing
The keowing and the cooing
There was a mewtiful beaumont
Of queace and pie-ate

Trevor Millum

Victoria's Poem

Send me upstairs without any tea,
refuse me a plaster to stick on my knee.

Make me kiss Grandpa who smells of his pipe,
make me eat beetroot, make me eat tripe.

Throw all my best dolls into the river.
Make me eat bacon and onions – with liver.

Tell Mr Allan I've been a bad girl,
rename me Nellie, rename me Pearl.

    But don't, even if
    the world suddenly ends
         ever again,
            Mother,
    wipe my face with a tissue
    in front of my friends.

Fred Sedgwick

I Saw a Jolly Hunter

I saw a jolly hunter
With a jolly gun
Walking in the country
In the jolly sun.

In the jolly meadow
Sat a jolly hare.
Saw the jolly hunter
Took jolly care.

Hunter jolly eager –
Sight of jolly prey.
Forgot gun pointing
Wrong jolly way.

Jolly hunter jolly head
Over heels gone.
Jolly old safety-catch
Not jolly on.

Bang went the jolly gun.
Hunter jolly dead.
Jolly hare got clean away.
Jolly good, I said.

Charles Causley

Kisses!

Last week,
my face was smother covered in kisses.
YES KISSES!
(Why do girls like to kiss so much?)
First there was the dribbly-wibbly kiss,
when Mum slurped all over me
like an eight-mouthed octopus. ('There's a good
   boy.')
Then there was the lipstick-redstick kiss,
when Aunty's rosy lips
painted themselves on my cheeks. ('Isn't he cute?')
Next came the flutter-eye-butterfly kiss.
when my girlfriend smoochy cooched
and fluttered her eyelashes at the same time.
('OOOOOOOO!')
After that there was the soggy-doggy kiss,
when our pet Labrador tried to lick my face off.
   ('Slop-woof.')
Following that there was the 'watch out here I
   come' miss-kiss,
when my little sister aimed for me
but missed and kissed the cat instead.
   ('UUUUUURGH!')
Then there was the spectacular-Dracula kiss,
when my brother leapt from behind the shower
   curtain
and attacked my neck. ('AAAAAAAGH-SUCK!')

Of course there was the 'sssssh don't tell anyone'
   self-kiss,
when I looked in the bathroom mirror
And kissed myself. ('Once was enough.')
But the unbeatable, second to none, zing-dinger of
   a kiss
came from Gran.
It was a lip sucking, cheek plucking, Donald
   Ducking
SMACKEROONY OF A KISS.
She'd forgotten to put her teeth in!

Ian Souter

Smile

Smile, go on, smile!
Anyone would think, to look at you,
that your cat was on the barbecue
or your best friend had died.
Go on, curve your mouth.
Take a look at that beggar,
or that one-legged bus conductor.
Where's *your* cross?
Smile, slap your thigh.
Hiccup, make a horse noise,
lollop through the house,
fizz up your coffee.
Take down your guitar
from its air-shelf and play
imaginary reggae
out through the open door.
And smile, remember, smile,
give those teeth some sun,
grin at everyone,
do it now, go on, SMILE!

Matthew Sweeney

Christmas Pudding

It lay on the table
proudly displayed.
'The best Christmas pudding,'
said Mum, 'ever made.

'You'll all find out
just how good in a minute,
for I've put some special
ingredients in it.'

It did seem sort
of strange somehow.
I couldn't quite
describe it now —

like something from
the fourth dimension.
'It is,' said Mum
'my own invention.

'You'll all remember
this — don't doubt it!'
Gran peered. 'There's something
odd about it.'

'Well, here we go,'
smiled Mum with pride
and grasped the knife
that lay beside.

'This is how puddings
should be made.'
The candlelight
gleamed off the blade.

There was a hush.
Time seemed to stop.
The knife blade touched
the pudding top.

The room shook in
a blinding flash,
a huge bang
and a mighty crash.

'Aliens!' I thought.
'Is my laser loaded?'
But no — the pudding
had exploded.

We sat there stunned
in frozen poses.
Bits of it
were up our noses.

Mum looked very
close to tears.
Bits of it
were in our ears.

Bits of it
dropped down the chair.
Bits of it
were in our hair.

Still no one moved
from where we sat.
Bits of it
were on the cat.

'Well then,' said Dad,
'no need to wait.'
Yes — bits of it
were on each plate.

'You're right, dear. Each
year in December,
this is a dish
that we'll remember.'

Bits covered the table
like lumpy lacquer.
'Very clever — a Christmas
pudding cracker.'

Charles Thomson

Give Yourself
a Hug

Give yourself a hug
when you feel unloved

Give yourself a hug
when people put on airs
to make you feel a bug

Give yourself a hug
when everyone seems to give you
a cold-shoulder shrug

Give yourself a hug –
a big big hug

And keep on singing,
'Only one in a million like me
Only one in a million-billion-trillion-zillion
Like me.'

Grace Nichols

An Accident

The playground noise stilled.
A teacher ran to the spot
beneath the climbing frame
where Rawinda lay, motionless.
We crowded around, silent,
gazing at the trickle of blood
oozing its way onto the tarmac.
Red-faced, the teacher shouted,
'Move back . . . get out of the way!'
and carried Rawinda into school,
limbs floppy as a rag doll's,
a red gash on her black face.

Later we heard she was at home,
five stitches in her forehead.
After school that day
Jane and I stopped beside the frame
and stared at the dark stain
shaped like a map of Ireland.
'Doesn't look much like blood,'
muttered Jane. I shrugged,
and remember now how warm it was
that afternoon, the white clouds,
and how sunlight glinted
from the polished bars.

We took Rawinda's 'Get Well' card
to her house. She was in bed,
quiet, propped up on pillows,
a white plaster on her dark skin.

Three days later
she was back at school,
her usual self, laughing,
twirling expertly on the bars,
wearing her plaster with pride,
covering for a week the scar,
she would keep for ever,
memento of a July day at school.

Wes Magee

A Better Mousetrap

If you build a better mousetrap
And put it in your house,
Before long, Mother Nature's
Going to build a better mouse.

Anon

I Saw a Ship a-Sailing

I saw a ship a-sailing,
A-sailing on the sea;
And, oh! it was laden
With pretty things for me.

There were comfits in the cabin,
And apples in the hold;
The sails were made of silk,
And the masts were made of gold.

The four-and-twenty sailors
That stood between the decks,
Were four-and-twenty white mice,
With chains about their necks.

The Captain was a duck,
With a packet on his back,
And when the ship began to move,
The Captain said, 'Quack, quack!'

Anon

The Fibber

She calls them bits of fiction
she calls them porky-pies
she calls them super-stories
but she never calls them lies.

The budgie ate her homework
she couldn't believe her eyes,
it made such a mess of his inside bits
that now he never flies.

Her dad's a racing driver.
He races her to school.
He drives at 90 miles per hour
and uses tons of fuel.

She says that when she's grown up
she wants to be a writer
and get paid to make things up all day,
it's a job which quite excites her.

Or she might go into politics
(after her misspent youth)
or some other nice profession
where they seldom tell the truth.

And on her 60th birthday
when she claims she's 43
those 17 long years
will disappear conveniently.

And when she's finally in her grave
and buried six feet deep,
they'll write on her stone the final fib:

NOT DEAD
BUT JUST ASLEEP

Lindsay MacRae

The Lobster Quadrille

'Will you walk a little faster?' said a whiting to a
   snail,
'There's a porpoise close behind us, and he's
   treading on my tail.
See how eagerly the lobsters and the turtles all
   advance!
They are waiting on the shingle — will you come
   and join the dance?
   Will you, won't you, will you, won't you, will
      you join the dance?
   Will you, won't you, will you, won't you, won't
      you join the dance?

'You can really have no notion how delightful it
    will be
When they take us up and throw us, with the
    lobsters, out to sea!'
But the snail replied 'Too far, too far!', and gave a
    look askance —
Said he thanked the whiting kindly, but he would
    not join the dance.
    Would not, could not, would not, could not,
        would not join the dance.
    Would not, could not, would not, could not,
        could not join the dance.

'What matters it how far we go?' his scaly friend
    replied.
'There is another shore, you know, upon the other
    side.
The further off from England the nearer is to
    France —
Then turn not pale, beloved snail, but come and
    join the dance.
    Will you, won't you, will you, won't you, will
        you join the dance?
    Will you, won't you, will you, won't you, won't
        you join the dance?'

Lewis Carroll

Otter

We found you at the edge of the road
Caught, out of your element,
By a car that roared past in the night.

In water, your sleek, supple shape
Darted at trout and
Flashed around moss-covered boulders;
Plunged over rapids.

Your silver pelt glimmered
In peat-brown deeps
Twisting and turning under cascades.

Now you are still and your fur is dark
Your unseeing eyes look up;
Mouth open wide,
Sharp, blood-covered teeth
Bared in a final snarl.

Calum Brown (9)

Ode to a Sneeze

I sneezed a sneeze into the air,
It fell to earth I know not where,
But hard and froze were the looks of those
In whose vicinity I snoze.

Anon

Pet Shop

At our pet shop you can buy
Things that run and swim and fly,
But never once have I seen them sell
Anything as big as an el-
ephant or albatross,
Crocodile, bear, rhinoceros,
Nor ever a creature as small, alas,
As a kingfisher, or grass-
hopper, earwig, bumble-bee,
Minnow, mole, or common flea.
O, I really think it is absurd
They don't keep a whale or a ladybird.

Leonard Clark

Chips

Out of the paper bag
Comes the hot breath of the chips
And I shall blow on them
To stop them burning my lips.

Before I leave the counter
The woman shakes
Raindrops of vinegar on them
And salty snowflakes.

Outside the frosty pavements
Are slippery as a slide
But the chips and I
Are warm inside.

Stanley Cook

Short Poem

Short poems
are fun.
You can see
at a glance
whether you
like them
or not.

Steve Turner

Small, Smaller

I thought that I knew all there was to know
Of being small, until I saw once, black against the
  snow,
A shrew, trapped in my footprint, jump and fall
And jump again and fall, the hole too deep, the
  walls too tall.

Russell Hoban

Electric Full Stops!

Nose pressed flat
Against the window,
All the way
From London to York;
I sat, rocked
By the rhythm of the track,
And teased
By the tilted, toothless grin
Of the cheeky Moon, on its back.
A train flashed past,
Like a blurred arrow of light,
Weaving through the cold January night;
Weaving through the miles of blackness,
Punctuated only
By amber dots,
Hovering,
Like a million electric full stops.

Nisha Doshi (8)

The Woodman's Dog

Shaggy, and lean, and shrewd, with pointed ears,
And tail cropp'd short, half lurcher and half cur —
His dog attends him. Close behind his heel
Now creeps he slow; and now, with many a frisk
Wide-scampering, snatches up the drifted snow
With ivory teeth, or ploughs it with his snout;
Then shakes his powder'd coat, and barks for joy.

William Cowper

Cat!

Cat!
Scat!
Atter her, atter her,
Sleeky flatterer,
Spitfire chatterer,
Scatter her, scatter her
  Off her mat!
   Wuff!
   Wuff!
  Treat her rough!
Git her, git her,
Whiskery spitter!
Catch her, catch her,
Green-eyed scratcher!
  Slathery
  Slithery
  Hisser,
  Don't miss her!
Run till you're dithery,
  Hithery
  Thithery
  Pfitts! Pfitts!
  How she spits!
  Spitch! Spatch!
  Can't she scratch!

Scritching the bark
Of the sycamore-tree,
She's reached her ark
And's hissing at me
   Pfitts! Pfitts!
   Wuff! Wuff!
      Scat,
      Cat!
      That's
      That!

Eleanor Farjeon

The Story of Augustus Who Would Not Have Any Soup

Augustus was a chubby lad;
Fat ruddy cheeks Augustus had:
And everybody saw with joy
The plump and hearty, healthy boy.
He ate and drank as he was told,
And never let his soup get cold.
But one day, one cold winter's day,
He screamed out 'Take the soup away!
O take the nasty soup away!
I won't have any soup today.'

Next day, now look, the picture shows
How lank and lean Augustus grows!
Yet, though he feels so weak and ill,
The naughty fellow cries out still
'Not any soup for me, I say:
O take the nasty soup away!
I *won't* have any soup today.'

The third day comes: Oh what a sin!
To make himself so pale and thin.
Yet, when the soup is put on table,
He screams, as loud as he is able,
'Not any soup for me, I say:
O take the nasty soup away!
I WON'T have any soup today.'

Look at him, now the fourth day's come!
He scarcely weighs a sugar-plum;
He's like a little bit of thread,
And, on the fifth day, he was – dead!

Heinrich Hoffmann

My Dad the Headmaster

My dad the Headmaster knows every single rule
and when he is at home he thinks that he's at
  school.
He rings the bell each morning and I'd better not
  be late
so I'm washed and down for breakfast at exactly
  ten to eight.

He stands and takes the register, checks my shirt
  and tie,
then he says 'Good Morning' and I have to reply
'Good-Mor-ning-Fa-ther' in that monotone drone
and hear his assembly in my very own home.

He has a list of rules that are pasted on each door:
No Spitting. No Chewing. No Litter On The
  Floor.
No Music. No Jewellery. No Make-Up. No Telly.
No Making Rude Noises Especially If They're
  Smelly.

No Videos. No Football. No Coloured Socks Or
  Laces.
No Trainers. No Jeans. No Smiling Faces.
No Sticking Bubble Gum In Your Sister's Hair.
No Wiping Bogies Down The Side Of The Chair.

He has a list of sayings for all types of occasion
and a set of phrases for every situation:
'Don't run down the stairs. Speak when spoken to.
Put your hand up first if you want to use the loo.

'I don't mind how long I wait. Listen when I'm
   speaking.
No one leaves the table until we've finished eating.
Don't interrupt and don't answer back.
Don't do this and don't do that.'

Yes, my dad the Headmaster knows every single
   rule
and when he is at home he thinks that he's at
   school.
But I am not the only one who does what he is
   told.
Dad never complains if his dinner is cold.

He's ever so polite when mother is around
and mumbles 'Yes my dear' while looking at the
   ground.
Her foghorn commands, they really drive him
   crazy.
Dad's scared stiff of Mum . . . she's a dinner lady!

Paul Cookson

The Cat's Muse

*And the fat
cat musing on the mat
sang
(flat):*

I'm a tabby flabby house cat, just a fusty ball of
    fur,
A never-caught-a-mouse cat with a rusty sort of
    purr.
But sit down on the hearth mat and watch the fire
    with me.
I'll show you some of the dark and wild cats up
    my family tree.

Oh I'm no common-or-garden cat.
There's something you might miss:
The sabre teeth that I unsheathe
When I stretch and yawn like this.

Sheba was a temple cat in Tutankhamun's days.
She had a hundred priestesses and several hundred
    slaves.
She curled up on an altar on a bed of purple silk,
Off saucers made of beaten gold she dined on
    camel's milk.

Oh I'm no common-or-garden cat.
My pedigree tends to show.
My tail is like a cobra
when it lashes to and fro.

Captain Moggan was a ship's cat and he sailed the
  Spanish Main.
He went all the way around Cape Horn and made
  it home again.
His claws were sharp as cutlasses. His life was
  sharp and short.
He died in Valparaiso, leaving kittens in every
  port.

Oh I'm no common-or-garden cat.
Haven't you noticed my
One lop ear like a pirate's hat
That flops across my eye?

Greymalkin was a black magic cat with fur as slick
    as pitch.
She held covens in a cavern with a wild and
    wicked witch.
And when she went out hunting on a moonlit
    winter's night
The village folk would bar their doors and dogs
    dropped dead with fright.

Oh I'm no common-or-garden cat.
Who knows what I might do?
You'd better keep me happy
or I'll put a spell . . .
                    . . . on . . .
                        . . . YOU!

Philip Gross

Alone

The sun has been punctured
sagged out of sight behind the clouds.

I'm alone in the house
watching the moon lay long, cold fingers

Onto the curtains through the glass
in the creaking windows.

If the footsteps outside come up the path
I'm going to hide under my bed.

If the hand I can hear tapping a key
turns the lock and opens the door

I'm going to scamper along the landing
shove the bolt tight on the bathroom door

If the voice I can hear breathing hard
hisses and whispers up the stairs

I'm going to scramble down the drainpipe
and run for cover in the back garden.

Monsters are clever, these two for example
set their trap by calling my name

In the exact voice of my dad home from work
and of my mum back from the shops.

But I know their tricks, they won't catch me
although I suppose not many monsters

Bang and kick on the bathroom door
yelling 'Why at eleven years of age

Do we still have to go through this nonsense
each time one of us nips to the shops?'

Perhaps I've got it wrong
again.

David Harmer

I Dream of a Time

I dream of a time

When the only blades are blades of corn
When the only barrels are barrels of wine
When the only tanks are full of water
When the only chains are chains of hands

I hope for a time . . .

John Foster

Rat it Up

C'mon everybody
Slap some grease on those paws
Get some yellow on your teeth
And, uh, sharpen up your claws

There's a whole lot of sausage
We're gonna swallow down
We're going to jump out of the sewers
And rock this town

Cos we're ratting it up
Yes we're ratting it up
Well we're ratting it up
For a ratting good time tonight

Ain't got no compass
You don't need no map
Just follow your snout
Hey, watch out for that trap!

You can take out a poodle
You can beat up a cat
But if you can't lick a ferret
You ain't no kind of rat

Cos we're ratting it up
Yes we're ratting it up
Well we're ratting it up
For a ratting good time tonight

Now you can sneak in the henhouse
You can roll out the eggs
But if the farmer comes running
Bite his hairy legs

Check that cheese for poison
Before you eat
Or you'll wind up being served up
As ratburger meat

Cos we're ratting it up
Yes we're ratting it up
Well we're ratting it up
For a ratting good time tonight

This rat was born to rock
This rat was born to roll
I don't give a monkey's
Bout your pest control

So push off pussy-cat
Push off pup
We're the Rocking Rodents
And we're ratting it up

Yeah we're ratting it up
Yeah we're ratting it up
Well we're ratting it up
For a ratting good time tonight!

Adrian Mitchell

Way Down South

Way down south where the ripe bananas grow
An ant stepped on an elephant's toe.
The elephant cried with tears in his eyes
'Pick on somebody your own size.'

Anon

What Teachers Wear in Bed!

It's anybody's guess
what teachers wear in bed at night,
so we held a competition
to see if any of us were right.

We did a spot of research,
although some of them wouldn't say,
but it's probably something funny
as they look pretty strange by day.

Our headteacher's quite old fashioned,
he wears a Victorian nightshirt,
our sports teacher wears her tracksuit
and sometimes her netball skirt.

That new teacher in the infants
wears bedsocks with see-through pyjamas,
our deputy head wears a T-shirt
he brought back from the Bahamas.

We asked our secretary what she wore
but she shooed us out of her room,
and our teacher said, her favourite nightie
and a splash of expensive perfume.

And Mademoiselle, who teaches French,
is really very rude,
she whispered, 'Alors! Don't tell a soul,
but I sleep in the . . . back bedroom!'

Brian Moses

There Was An Old Man . . .

There was an Old Man with a beard,
Who said, 'It is just as I feared! —
   Two Owls and a Hen,
   four Larks and a Wren,
Have all built their nests in my beard!'

Edward Lear

The Land of Counterpane

When I was sick and lay a-bed,
I had two pillows at my head,
And all my toys beside me lay
To keep me happy all the day.

And sometimes for an hour or so
I watched my leaden soldiers go,
With different uniforms and drills,
Among the bed-clothes, through the hills;

And sometimes sent my ships in fleets
All up and down among the sheets;
Or brought my trees and houses out,
And planted cities all about.

I was the giant great and still
That sits upon the pillow-hill,
And sees before him, dale and plain,
The pleasant land of counterpane.

R. L. Stevenson

The Pobble Who Has No Toes

The Pobble who has no toes
    Had once as many as we;
When they said, 'Some day you may lose
    them all;' –
    He replied, – 'Fish fiddle de-dee!'
And his Aunt Jobiska made him drink,
Lavender water tinged with pink,
For she said, 'The world in general knows
There's nothing so good for a Pobble's toes!'

The Pobble who has no toes,
    Swam across the Bristol Channel;
But before he set out he wrapped his nose,
    In a piece of scarlet flannel.
For his Aunt Jobiska said, 'No harm
Can come to his toes if his nose is warm;
And it's perfectly known that a Pobble's toes
Are safe, – provided he minds his nose.'

The Pobble swam fast and well
    And when boats and ships come near him
He tinkledy-binkledy-winkled a bell
    So that all the world could hear him.
And all the Sailors and Admirals cried,
When they saw him nearing the further side, –
'He has gone to fish, for his Aunt Jobiska's
Runcible Cat with crimson whiskers!'

But before he touched the shore,
    The shore of the Bristol Channel,
A sea-green Porpoise carried away
    His wrapper of scarlet flannel.
And when he came to observe his feet
Formerly garnished with toes so neat
His face at once became forlorn
On perceiving that all his toes were gone!

And nobody ever knew
    From that dark day to the present,
Whoso had taken the Pobble's toes,
    In a manner far from pleasant.
Whether the shrimps or crawfish grey,
Or crafty Mermaids stole them away -
Nobody knew; and nobody knows
How the Pobble was robbed of his twice five toes!

The Pobble who has no toes
    Was placed in a friendly Bark,
And they rowed him back, and carried him up,
    To his Aunt Jobiska's Park.
And she made him a feast of his earnest wish
Of eggs and buttercups fried with fish; —
And she said, — 'It's a fact the whole world knows,
That Pobbles are happier without their toes.'

Edward Lear

The Child Who Pretended
to be a Dragon

My mum and dad got angry
and they told me not to lie,
when I said that I'd grown wings
and was learning how to fly.

They said I should be sensible
and stop making a fuss,
after I'd announced that I was green
and longer than a bus.

And they turned around and told me
I was not to tell tall tales,
when they heard that I'd been claiming
that my skin was growing scales.

Then both of them got cross with me
and each called me a liar,
just because I mentioned
I'd been breathing smoke and fire.

But they finally got flaming mad,
they really hit the roof
when I rushed at them with sharpened claws
and all my teeth, as proof.

My mum let out a piercing scream.
My dad began to rave.
So I ate them both. They tasted nice.
Then I flew off to live in a cave.

Nick Toczek

Longing

I wish I was a litlle grub
With whiskers around my tummy
I'd climb into a honey-pot
And make my tummy gummy.

Anon

Football Through the Ages

Football grew from itchy feet
kicking whatever they found in the street;
a pebble; a stick; a rolling stone;
a rusty can or an animal's bone.
The left-over bladder of a butchered pig,
inflated and tied off, was perfect to kick;
if something would roll it would do for the game
that then had not even been given a name
till, on through the ages, the game was to grow,
at long last becoming the football we know.

O, I'm glad of my football, I'm glad of the rules,
I'm glad of the pitches at clubs and at schools,
I'm glad of my kit, but I am even gladder
the days are long gone when they kicked a
   pig's bladder.

Celia Warren

The Camel

The camel has a single hump;
The dromedary, two;
Or else the other way around.
I'm never sure. Are you?

Ogden Nash

Lines

I must never daydream in schooltime.
I just love a daydream in Mayshine.
I must ever greydream in timeschool.
Why must others paydream in schoolway?
Just over highschool dismay lay.
Thrust over skydreams in cryschool.
Cry dust over drydreams in screamtime.
Dreamschool thirst first in dismayday.
Why lie for greyday in crimedream?
My time for dreamday is soontime.
In soontime must I daydream ever.
Never must I say dream in strifetime.
Cry dust over daydreams of lifetimes.
I must never daydream in schooltime.
In time I must daydream never.

Judith Nicholls

I Think I Could Turn and Live With Animals

I think I could turn and live with animals,
    they're so placid and self-contained,
I stand and look at them long and long.

They do not sweat and whine about
    their condition,
They do not lie awake in the dark and weep
    for their sins,
They do not make me sick discussing their
    duty to God,
Not one is dissatisfied, not one is demented
    with the mania of owning things,
Not one kneels to another, nor to his kind
    that lived thousands of years ago,
Not one is respectable or unhappy over the
    whole earth.

Walt Whitman

Someone Stole The

While I was taking a short   -nap
  someone stole the   ,
I should have spun round like a   herine wheel
when someone stole the   .
But I was too slow to   ch them,
  . when someone stole the   .

Now the   amaran can't float,
  because someone stole the   .
And the   erpillar can't crawl,
  because someone stole the   .
And the   aract can't fall,
  because someone stole the   .

It was not me and it was not you
but it is   egorically true,
And if you were to ask me
  I'd say it was a   astrophe
That someone's stolen the   .

Brian Patten

Daisies and Grasses

Daisies so bright,
Grasses so green,
Tell me, I pray,
How you keep clean?

Summertime showers,
Summertime rain,
Wash dusty flowers
All clean again.

Anon

Amy Elizabeth Ermyntrude Annie

Amy Elizabeth Ermyntrude Annie
Went to the country to visit her Grannie;

Learnt to churn butter and learnt to make cheese,
Learnt to milk cows and take honey from bees;

Learnt to spice roseleaves and learnt to cure ham,
Learnt to make cider and black-currant jam.

When she came home she could not settle down,
Said there was nothing to do in the town.

Nothing to do there and nothing to see:
Life was all shopping and afternoon tea!

Amy Elizabeth Ermyntrude Annie
Ran away back to the country and Grannie!

Queenie Scott-Hopper

Down with Flu!

I've a bag code,
fluey and flemmy
in me node;

feel like somebobby's
stuffed
a hod wet towel
insibe
me achin' heb;

I've a scratchy frob
in me throbe,
me chest's full
ob frobspawn;

I wheeze and explose
ashoo–ashoo–ashoo
into me hankersneeze,
I tishoo-tishoo-tishoo
into me tishoo;

I've a bag code
in me node,
and I'm feb up,
really feb up,

really, really, really
feb up here in beb.

Matt Simpson

Pool Players

Some say
Ullapool's
a duller pool
than Liverpool
but give a pool
a chance!

I say
Ullapool's
a filled-with-life-
and-colour pool
where people sing
and dance.

Some say
Hartlepool's
an only-just-
and-partly pool
but give a pool
a break!

I say
Hartlepool's
a look-alive-
and-smartly pool
where folk are wide
awake.

As every Hartlepudlian
and every Ullapudlian
and every Liverpudlian

knows, for heaven's sake!

Kit Wright

Snow

In the gloom of whiteness,
In the great silence of snow,
A child was sighing
And bitterly saying: 'Oh,
They have killed a white bird up there on her nest,
The down is fluttering from her breast!'
And still it fell through that dusky brightness
On the child crying for the bird of the snow.

Edward Thomas

Polly

Polly had a dolly
That was sick-sick-sick
So she telephoned the doctor
To come quick-quick-quick.

Round came the doctor
With his bag and hat
And he rapped on the door
With a rat-ta-tat-tat.

He looked at Polly's dolly
And this is what he said
'Polly put your dolly
Into bed-bed-bed.'

'Here is the paper
For a pill-pill-pill
And I'll see you tomorrow
With my bill-bill-bill.'

Anon

Four Little Tigers

Four little tigers
  Sitting in a tree;
One became a lady's coat —
  Now there's only three.

Three little tigers
  Neath a sky of blue:
One became a rich man's rug —
  Now there's only two.

Two little tigers
  Sleeping in the sun:
One a hunter's trophy made —
  Now there's only one.

One little tiger
  Waiting to be had:
Oops! He got the hunter first —
  Aren't you kind of glad?

Frank Jacobs

Thirty Days Hath September

Thirty days hath September,
April, June, and November;
February has twenty-eight alone,
All the rest have thirty-one,
Excepting Leap-year, that's the time
When February's days are twenty-nine.

Anon

The Codfish

The codfish lays ten thousand eggs,
    The homely hen lays one.
The codfish never cackles
    To tell you what she's done.
And so we scorn the codfish,
    While the humble hen we prize,
Which only goes to show you
    That it pays to advertise.

Anon

Say, Did You Say?

Say, did you say, or did you not say
What I said you said?
For it is said that you said
That you did not say
What I said you said.
Now if you say that you did not say
What I said you said,
Then what do you say you did say instead
Of what I said you said?

Anon

Acknowledgements

The compiler and publishers wish to thank the following for permission to use copyright material:

John Agard, 'Secret' from *Get Back Pimple*, Viking (1995), by permission Caroline Sheldon Literary Agency on behalf of the author; **Allan Ahlberg**, 'Glenis' from *Please Mrs Butler* by Allan Ahlberg, Kestrel (1983) p.23. Copyright © Allan Ahlberg, 1983, by permission of Penguin Books; **George Mackay Brown**, 'Beachcomber' from *Selected Poems*, by permission of John Murray (Publishers) Ltd; **Calum Brown**, 'Otter' from *S is an Anaconda* (1992) Young Writers Competition, by permission of W H Smith; **David Calder**, 'Good Morning, this is the teacher forecast'. Copyright © David Calder 1994, by permission of the author; **Charles Causley**, 'I Saw a Jolly Hunter' and 'Good Morning, Mr Croco-doco-dile' from *Collected Poems for Children* by Charles Causley, Macmillan, by permission of David Higham Associates on behalf of the author; **Leonard Clark**, 'Pet Shop', by permission of Robert Clark; **John Coldwell**, 'The Disco Sheep', by permission of the author; **Paul Cookson**, 'My Dad the Headmaster', first published in *More Secret Lives of Teachers*, ed. Brian Moses, Macmillan, by permission of the author; **Peter Dixon**, 'Tadpoles' from *Grand Prix* by Peter Dixon, Macmillan, by permission of the author; **Nisha Doshi**, 'Electric Full Stops!' from *Electric Full Stops!* (1995), Young Writers Competition, by permission of W H Smith; **James Emtage**, 'Birthdays' from *S is an Anaconda* (1992), Young Writers Competition, by permission of W H Smith; **Eleanor Farjeon**, 'Cat!' from *Blackbird Has Spoken*, Macmillan, by permission of David Higham Associates on behalf of the author; **Max Fatchen**, 'Pussy Cat, Pussy Cat' from *Peculiar Rhymes and Lunatic Lines* by Max Fatchen, Orchard Books, by permission of The Watts Publishing Group Ltd; **John Foster**, 'I Dream of a Time' first published in *Can You Hear?: Poems for Oxfam*, Macmillan. Copyright © 1992 John Foster, by permission of the author; **Mick Gowar**, 'New Leaf' from *Third Time Lucky* by Mick Gowar, Viking Kestrel (1988) Copyright © Mick Gowar, 1988, by permission of Penguin Books; **David Harmer**, 'Alone', by permission of the author; **Adrian Henri**, 'Square Meal' from *The Phantom Lollipop Lady*, Methuen. Copyright © Adrian Henri, 1986, by permission of Rogers Coleridge & White Ltd on behalf of the author; **Russell Hoban**, 'Small, Smaller' from *The Pedalling Man*, Heinemann, by permission of David Higham Associates on behalf of the author; **Rudyard Kipling**, 'Thy Servant a Dog', by permission of A P Watt on behalf of The National Trust for Places of Historic Interest or Natural Beauty; **Shelagh McGee**, 'Wanted – A Witch's Cat' from *What Witches Do*, Felix Gluck Press, by permission of the author; **Roger McGough**, 'Having My Ears Boxed' from *Sky in the Pie*, Kestrel (1983), by permission of of Peters Fraser & Dunlop Group Ltd on behalf of the author;